This book belongs to
BETHaNY

make believe ideas ltd
The Wilderness, Berkhamsted, Hertfordshire, HP4 2AZ, UK.

www.makebelieveideas.com

Written by Holly Lansley.
Illustrated by Lara Ede.

Follow the Star
Lara Ede • Holly Lansley
make believe ideas

Once a girl of special worth
heard from an angel she'd give birth
to Jesus, God's own Son on earth,
who'd be our King one day.

The girl, called **Mary**, had been blessed,
and told her **husband** of God's quest.
Joseph knew God's path was best,
and kept **faith** every day.

Mary grew as time went on,
and then a law called everyone...

Travel back to where you're from,
and leave without delay!

There was nothing they could do.
So the faithful pair, and donkey too,

Journeyed off into the blue
to find somewhere to stay.

But there was trouble still in store!
In Bethlehem they quickly saw
signs strung up on every door:
"No rooms free - GO AWAY!"

Full
No
vacancies
FULL

They thought they'd never find a space,
until a kind man showed them grace,
and gave them all a special place,
in a stable filled with hay.

There amongst the meek and mild,
Mary had her little child,
and God looked down on them and smiled
that special, holy day.

Up in heaven, angels **cheered**,

and **though** they knew that they'd be feared,

to some shepherds they appeared
and shone to light the grey.

The choir of angels told the herd:
"God's Son is here! Go spread the word!"

And everyone around was stirred
to visit straight away.

FULL
FULL

Far away, three wise men saw
a star that made them stop in awe.
The star would lead them to the door
where Baby Jesus lay.

With frankincense and gold that glowed,
as well as myrrh packed in their load,
through the desert, on they rode,
towards its shining ray.

When they finally saw the sight
of the baby born that night,
they knew that He was the true light,
and bent their knees to pray.

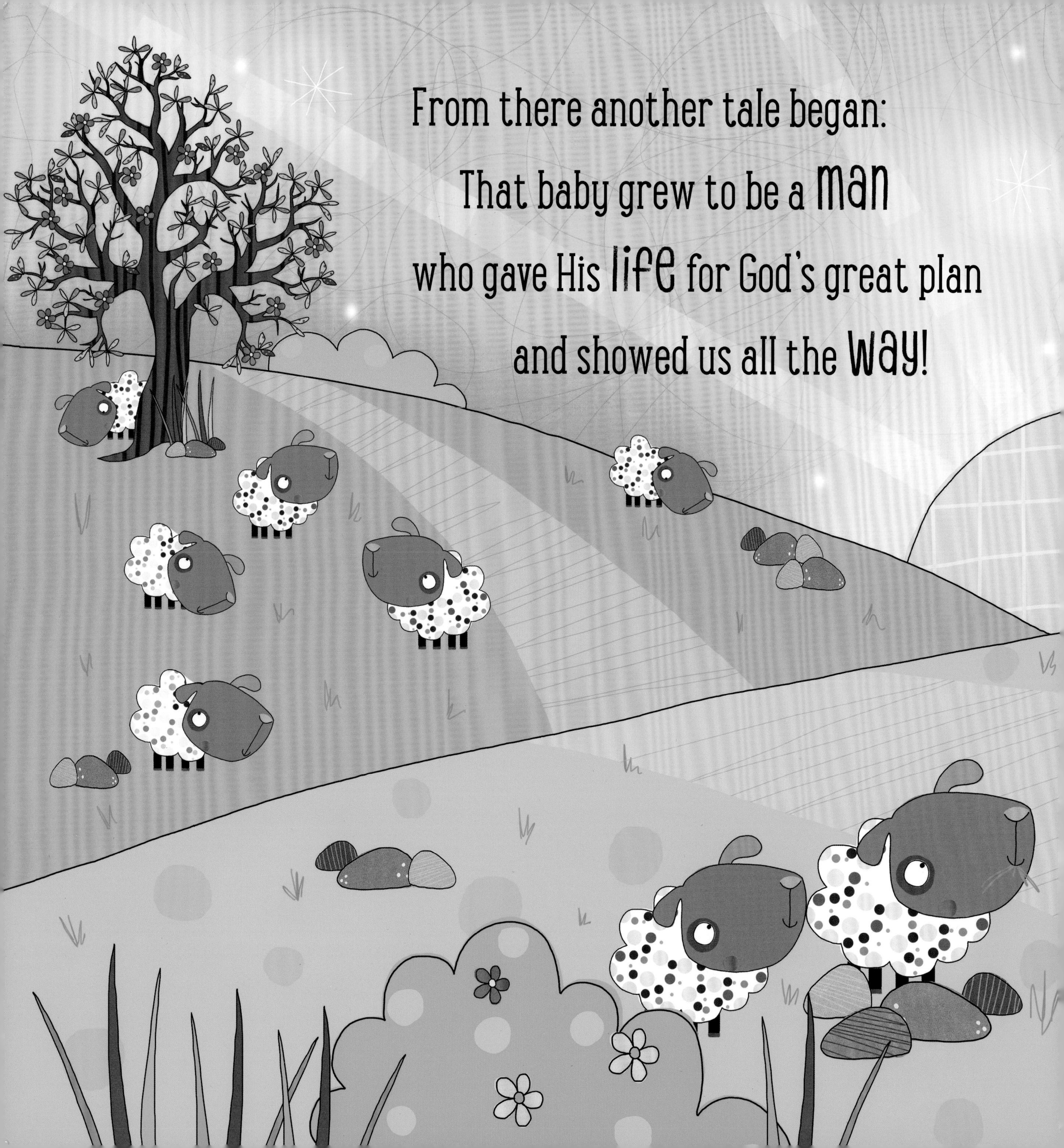
From there another tale began:
That baby grew to be a man
who gave His life for God's great plan
and showed us all the way!